Killer Croc

by

S. P. Gates

Illustrated by Dylan Gibson

To Laura, Alex and Chris

With special thanks to:

Edward Ainsworth
Rohom Audeshuzaleh
Shawn Brown
Luke browne
A?en Cankaya
Alast?? Davidson
Brian ??
Soif Jovic?
Susan ??
Liz Lewis
Aishah Liaqliet

Tarran Low
Nicole Maca??
Justine Marshall
Harry McLaughlin
Andrew McMillan
Nathan Napton
??
William Rodger
??b Shoukat
Nathan Sykes

This book was chosen by:

Name: Sam Hatcher

First published in 2009 in Great Britain by
Barrington Stoke Ltd
18 Walker St, Edinburgh, EH3 7LP

www.barringtonstoke.co.uk

Reprinted 2010

?? Gates

?? of the ?? for ?? ?? ?? in accordance with the Copyright, Designs and Patents Act ??

ISBN ??

Printed in Great Britain by Bell & Bain Ltd

Contents

Chapter 1
The Cool Cap

Levi told his mum, "I'm going out."

His mum said, "Don't go into that river. The Killer Croc will get you!"

"Mum, you've told me about that croc a million times," Levi said with a sigh.

Levi was thirteen and lived in a village in East Africa. Every kid in his village knew about the Killer Crocodile. He was the biggest croc in the river. He was old and sneaky. Most of the time, he snatched deer from the river banks. But last year, he'd snatched two children. They had never been seen again.

"Anyway, I'm not going down to the river," Levi told his mum. "I'm going to play football."

Levi pulled on his cap. He loved that cap. One day, a truck full of soldiers had passed through his village. After they'd gone, Levi had found the cap. It was lying in the road. Levi had picked it up.

The cap had a cool silver badge on it. It shone in the sun. When his mates saw it shining, they shouted to each other, "Hey, here's Levi coming!"

Levi said, "See you later, Mum. And don't worry. I'll keep away from that croc."

Chapter 2
"Are You Crazy?"

On his way to the football field, Levi saw the Killer Croc.

The croc was far away, across the river. It was sunbathing on the river bank. It looked slow and lazy. But Levi wasn't fooled. That old croc could run faster than an Olympic runner. And its teeth could crunch your bones.

After it snatched the two children, soldiers had been sent to shoot it. They looked for it for a week.

But Killer Croc was too sneaky for them.
It always got away.

Suddenly, a strong wind blew. It blew
the cap off Levi's head.

"My cap!" yelled Levi. He chased it. He
didn't want to lose his cap. It made him so
proud to wear it. No boy in the village had
one like it. And Levi had no money to buy
another.

Levi's cap blew down the river bank. It blew into the river. It was floating on the water. Levi could see the silver badge shining.

Levi stopped at the top of the bank. He remembered his mum's warning, "Don't go into the river."

But he had to get his cap back. So he climbed down the bank.

A little boy passing by said, "Are you crazy? Can't you see the Killer Croc over there?"

"He's asleep," said Levi. "I bet his belly is full. I bet he ate a deer this morning. He won't want to eat me."

Levi waded out into the river.

On the other bank, the Killer Croc
opened one eye. Without making any sound
at all, it slid into the river too.

Chapter 3
Croc Attack!

The cap bobbed down the river, its silver badge shining. Levi waded after it.

Once, he almost got it. But the river snatched it away again.

He didn't see the Killer Croc coming
after him. It slid through the water without
a sound. All you could see were its eyes and
nose.

Levi had almost got his cap again. It was
right in front of him. He put his hand out to
grab it.

Suddenly, the croc exploded out of the water, its mouth wide open.

Levi yelled. The Killer Croc snapped at his leg. Levi felt his skin rip and saw his blood turn the water red.

Levi tried to fight the croc. He punched its nose. It didn't let go.

Levi poked it in the eyes. But still that big old croc wouldn't let go. It pulled Levi under the water. It rolled over and over, trying to drown him, just like it did when it snatched a deer.

I'm dying, Levi thought.

Water went into his mouth. Everything went black. He passed out.

The little boy was still on the river bank. He saw the fight between Levi and the Killer Croc. He saw them both go under the water. He saw bubbles come up. Then the bubbles stopped. The little boy's eyes were wide with horror.

He went rushing back to the village shouting, "Levi is dead! Levi is dead! The Killer Croc got him!"

Chapter 4
The Killer Croc's Den

Levi opened his eyes. At first he just felt sick and dizzy.

Then he remembered the croc attack. *I'm still alive!* he thought, amazed.

He was lying in a little cave. It was very dark. There was a disgusting smell. He put out his hand.

"Ugggh!" He'd touched something cold and slimy. It was the rotting leg of a deer.

"Oh, no," whispered Levi. Now he knew where he was. He was in the Killer Croc's den, which was a hole among the tree roots in the river bank.

Crocodiles often bring food back to their den. They leave it there to rot. Then they can rip it apart easily.

Levi thought, *soon that old croc will be back to rip me up!*

He was shaking with fear. He tried to make himself calm. He told himself, "You must escape, before the Killer Croc comes back."

But was the croc outside, guarding its den?

That made Levi shake with fear all over again.

But he had to risk it. If he stayed here, he'd be dead, for sure.

Levi wriggled through the tree roots and out of the den.

He started to crawl up the bank.

But at the top was the Killer Croc, watching him. It seemed to have a big grin on its face.

Then it opened its mouth. It showed those terrible sharp teeth.

It started to slide down the bank.

Levi thought, *it's coming to get me!*

Levi dived into the river. He started swimming across it. He was swimming as fast as he could. But the croc was behind him, speeding through the water like a motor boat. Levi got to the other bank. He pulled himself out of the water.

I'm safe, he thought.

But the croc jumped, with its jaws open wide. It made a grab for Levi. It tore a bit off his shirt. Levi started running. But he was limping. His leg hurt where the croc had ripped it. His footprint was full of blood.

Levi couldn't outrun the croc. So he tried to lose it. He swerved, like he did playing football. He dived through bushes. He took a quick look back.

He couldn't believe it! That old Killer Croc was still behind him. It was running like a race horse, with a bit of his shirt in its jaws. It was catching him up!

Chapter 5
"I'm Trapped Up Here!"

Levi ran to a tree. He climbed up it.

Again he thought, *I'm safe!*

But the Killer Croc was right behind. It leapt two metres up into the air! It tore off Levi's trainer, then crunched it to bits in its teeth.

Levi climbed higher and higher. He sat shaking in the branches. He looked down. The Killer Croc was far below him. Even it couldn't jump this far.

Levi thought, *that croc must give up now*.

But it didn't. That old croc was hungry.
It wanted its dinner. It sat under the tree
and waited.

Levi's clothes were wet from the river.
His shirt was in rags. He only had one shoe.
His leg would not stop bleeding. He looked a
mess. He felt so weak and scared and
hopeless he could have cried like a baby.

Oh, no, it's getting dark now, he thought.
That's all I need!

He could hear wild dogs howling
somewhere. He could hear a lion roaring.
But they were a long way away. It was the
croc he was afraid of.

Levi told himself, "Don't fall asleep." If he fell asleep he'd fall out of the tree. That's just what that old croc was waiting for.

But he was so sleepy. Even the pain from his leg didn't keep him awake. His eyes closed, slowly, slowly ... Then he thought, *I'm slipping!* His eyes shot open.

He put out his hand to grab a branch. The branch moved! It hissed at him. Its tongue went in and out. It was a snake. It had been sleeping in the tree. Levi had woken it up.

It was a Green Mamba. Every kid in his village knew about Green Mambas. They were very dangerous. One bite from a Green Mamba could kill you. But Levi couldn't climb down the tree.

The Killer Croc was still down there. Levi could see its red eyes, glowing in the dark.

Levi thought, *I'm trapped up here!*

The Green Mamba slid towards Levi. He tried to stay very still and not make a sound. If he moved, or made a noise, the snake would bite him. It slid up his arm. Levi tried not to shudder. Its tongue went in and out.

Levi felt his hands shaking. He just couldn't help it.

Stay still, he told himself.

But his heart was beating like a big drum. He hoped the snake couldn't hear it.

The snake slid over his body, smelling

him with his tongue. Then it slid over his

bare foot. Then it slipped away down the tree.

"It's gone," whispered Levi, with a big sigh of relief.

Maybe that old croc had gone too. Maybe the snake had scared it away.

But that old croc wasn't scared of snakes. It wasn't scared of anything, even soldiers with guns. Levi heard a growl from out of the dark down there. It was the Killer Croc, walking round and round the tree. It was waiting for him to fall out. Then it would get him.

Levi pulled a long strand of creeping vine out of the tree. He used it like string to tie himself to the tree trunk.

"I won't fall out now!" he yelled down at the croc. "So why don't you go home?"

But the Killer Croc didn't go home. It stayed at the bottom of the tree, waiting. It knew Levi couldn't stay up there for ever. It knew it would get him, sooner or later.

Levi had tried to stay awake. But he just couldn't. Soon his eyes were closing, closing ... Then he was fast asleep.

Chapter 6
"Run!"

Suddenly Levi woke up. He could hear someone yelling! He looked around. It was daylight. He tried to move. But he was still tied to the tree with vines.

He looked down. There was a little girl down there, screaming her head off. She was from his village. She was pointing into

35

the tree, shouting, "It's a ghost! It's a

ghost!"

Like everyone else in the village, she thought Levi must be dead by now. No one had ever escaped from the Killer Croc.

"Watch out!" Levi yelled down at her. "Is that croc still around?"

He couldn't see it. Maybe it had got tired of waiting. Maybe it had given up and gone home, to its smelly den, in the river bank.

Levi untied the vine. He started climbing down the tree.

The little girl was still screaming, "It's a ghost."

"I'm not a ghost," said Levi. "I'm still alive. See?" He beat at his chest to show her.

"The croc didn't get me," he said proudly.

He was almost down the tree. Then he saw a big log on the ground behind the little girl. Only it wasn't a log. Suddenly its eyes opened. Its tail moved.

"It's the Killer Croc!" yelled Levi. "Run!"

But it was too late. The croc moved fast as lightning towards the little girl.

"Run!" yelled Levi again. But she was frozen with fear.

The croc's mouth opened wide, ready to bite her.

Then Levi heard yelling. A crowd of people ran out of the bushes. It was everyone from his village! They had been looking for him all night.

They charged at the croc, banging pots and pans, making a big noise. They shouted at it. They threw sticks and stones.

That big old croc didn't look scared. But at last it turned round. It walked slowly off into the bushes. The last thing Levi saw was a flick of its scaly tail.

He came down from the tree. His mum and dad were there.

His mum told him off. She was really angry. "I told you a thousand times not to go in that river!"

But then she threw her arms around him and started crying. She couldn't stop hugging him. "Oh, son," she said, "I was scared you were dead."

His dad hugged him too. "I can't believe you're alive," he said.

"That old Killer Croc couldn't get me," said Levi.

But secretly he thought, *It had a pretty good try!*

Chapter 7
The Silver Badge

After six weeks, Levi's leg got better.

He told his mum, "I'm going to play football with my mates."

But he wasn't going to play football. He was going down to the river again.

He wanted to look for his cap. He really missed wearing it. He didn't feel the same without it.

He thought, *maybe it's been washed up on the bank*.

He looked for its silver badge, shining in the sun. But he never saw it.

Sometimes he saw the Killer Croc far off, lazing about on a mud bank. But he kept well away. And he didn't go into the water. He knew how fast that old croc could move, if it wanted to. And he knew that, once it started to chase you, it never gave up.

Levi looked for days for his cap. But he never found it.

"Maybe it's at the bottom of the river," he said sadly. "Or maybe someone found it and kept it."

But like that old croc, he never gave up. Months later, he was still looking. Even though, in his heart, he knew it was hopeless.

Then, one day, his dad came back home from work.

"Do you know what?" he said to Levi. "That old Killer Croc is dead."

"You're kidding me!" said Levi. "Did the soldiers shoot it?"

"No," said his dad. "Someone found it on the river bank. It just died of old age. They cut it up for crocodile meat. And this is what they found in its belly."

Levi's dad took something out of his pocket. It was shiny and silver.

"It's my cap badge!" said Levi.

"It must have eaten your cap," said his dad. "And this is all that's left of it."

"And now I've got it back!" said Levi. "From inside that old croc's belly! I can't believe it! Thanks, Dad."

It wasn't the whole cap. But it was the next best thing.

Levi pinned the badge to his shirt. As he walked to the football field, his mates saw the badge shining.

"Hey!" they shouted to each other. "Here's Levi coming!"

He's faced the Killer Croc.
But there's lots more to come!

Join Levi in his next adventure –
this time a lion is out for his blood ...
Can Levi escape?

*Find out in the second book,
coming soon!*

For more info visit our website at
www.barringtonstoke.co.uk

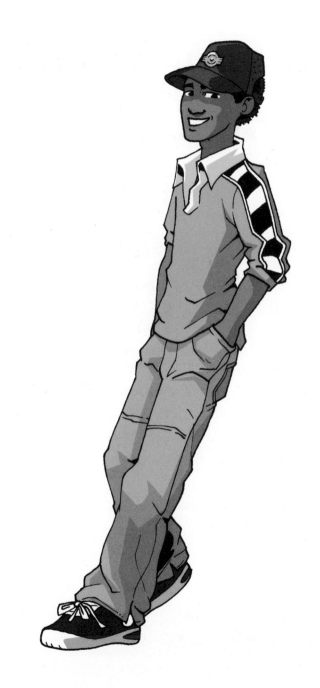

The Night Runner

by
Alan Combes

Greg wants to win the race. Every night
he trains in secret on the school field. But
he sees a spooky shape in the moon-light.
What is it? Should he run for his life?

You can order *The Night Runner* from our website at
www.barringtonstoke.co.uk

Cliff Edge

by
Jane A. C. West

Can Danny make the climb of his life to
save his friend? No ropes, no help –
no hope?

You can order *Cliff Edge* from our website at
www.barringtonstoke.co.uk

Snow Dogs

by
Jane A. C. West

Zeb wants to win the dog sled race. But
will he die before he gets
to the end?

You can order *Snow Dogs* from our website at
www.barringtonstoke.co.uk

Flash Flood

by
Andy Croft

Jaz and Toni are trapped and the water is rising ... Can they make it out in time?

You can order *Flash Flood* from our website at
www.barringtonstoke.co.uk